Christmas Around the Piano

arranged by Eugénie R. Rocherolle

General Words and Music Company • Neil A. Kjos Jr., Publisher • San Diego, California

Contents

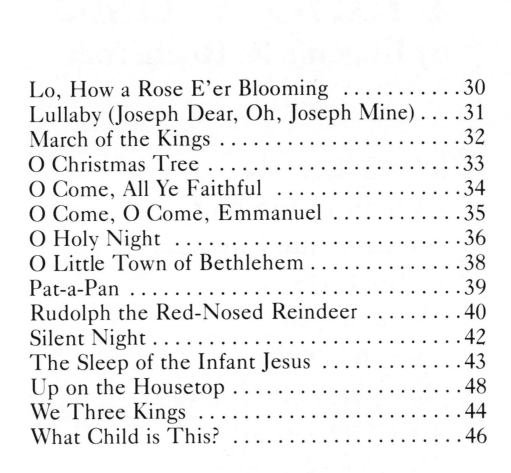

ISBN 0-8497-6141-7

Piano Music
by Eugénie R. Rocherolle

Solo Collections
American Sampler

Getting into Intervals

Miniatures

Montage

Seven Scenes

Six Moods for Piano

Duet Collection
Headin' South

Published by General Words and Music
Distributed by Kjos West, San Diego, Ca.

Eugénie Ricau Rocherolle, composer, pianist, and lyricist, began writing for the piano at an early age. She is partial to composing piano music and considers the piano her favorite instrument although her creative repertoire includes an impressive number of published pieces for chorus and for band, and unpublished scores for chamber groups, an operetta, and a musical comedy.

She is a member of American Society of Composers, Authors and Publishers and the National League of American Penwomen, and is included in the *International Encyclopedia of Women Composers*.

Born and raised in New Orleans, Mrs. Rocherolle graduated from Newcomb College of Tulane University, with a year of study in Paris. She and her husband, Didier, have four children and live in Connecticut.

Angels, from the Realms of Glory

1. Angels, from the realms of glory,
   Wing your flight o'er all the earth;
   Ye who sang creation's story,
   Now proclaim Messiah's birth:

   Refrain:
   Come and worship, come and worship,
   Worship Christ the newborn King.

2. Shepherds in the fields abiding,
   Watching o'er your flocks by night,
   God with man is now residing;
   Yonder shines the infant Light:

3. Sages, leave your contemplations;
   Brighter visions beam afar;
   Seek the great Desire of Nations;
   Ye have seen His natal star:

Words: James Montgomery

Music: Henry Smart

An "invention," the intention

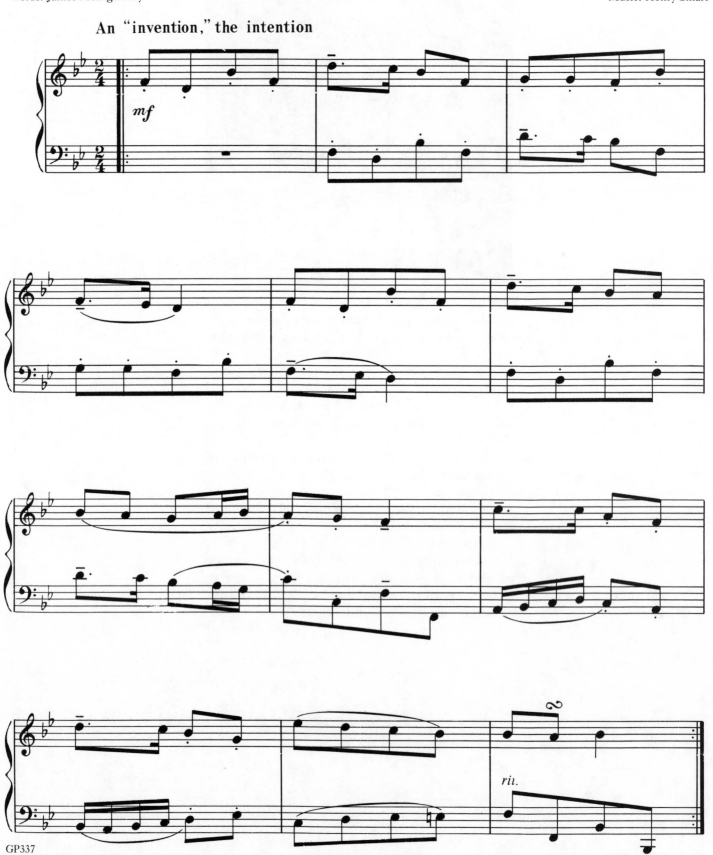

Angels We Have Heard on High

1. Angels we have heard on high,
   Sweetly singing o'er the plains,
   And the mountains in reply
   Echoing their joyous strains.

   Refrain:
   Gloria in excelsis Deo,
   Gloria in excelsis Deo.

2. Shepherds, why this jubilee?
   Why these songs of happy cheer?
   What great brightness did you see?
   What glad tidings did you hear?

3. Come to Bethlehem and see
   Him whose birth the angels sing;
   Come, adore on bended knee
   Christ, the Lord, the newborn King.

Words: Bishop Chadwick

Music: Traditional French Carol

Away in a Manger

1. Away in a manger, no crib for a bed.
   The little Lord Jesus laid down His sweet head;
   The stars in the sky looked down where He lay,
   The little Lord Jesus, asleep on the hay.

2. The cattle are lowing, the poor Baby wakes,
   But little Lord Jesus, no crying He makes;
   I love Thee, Lord Jesus! Look down from the sky,
   And stay by my cradle 'til morning is nigh.

3. I love Thee, Lord Jesus, I ask Thee to stay
   Close by me forever and love me I pray;
   Bless all the dear children in Thy tender care,
   And take us to heaven to live with Thee there.

Words: Martin Luther

Music: Traditional German

Bring a Torch, Jeanette, Isabella

1. Bring a torch, Jeanette, Isabella,
   Bring a torch to the cradle, run!
   It is Jesus, good folk of the village,
   Christ is born, and Mary's calling;
   Ah! Ah! Beautiful is the Mother!
   Ah! Ah! Beautiful is her Son!

2. Skies are glowing, the night is cloudless,
   Skies are glowing, come rise from your beds!
   Hasten all who would see the dear Christ Child,
   Shining and bright as yon lone star!
   Run, run! Put on your finest garments!
   Run, run! Presents for Jesus bring!

French Carol

GP337

Christmas Comes Anew

1. Christmas comes anew,
   O, let us sing Noel!
   Glory to God!
   Now let your praises swell!

   Refrain:
   Sing we Noel
   For Christ, the newborn King, Noel!
   Sing we Noel
   For Christ, the newborn King.
   Christmas comes anew,
   O, let us sing Noel!

2. Angels did say,
   "O shepherds, come and see,
   Born in Bethlehem,
   A blessed Lamb for thee."

3. In the manger bed,
   The shepherds found the Child;
   Joseph was there,
   And Mother Mary mild.

French Carol

Deck the Halls

1. Deck the halls with boughs of holly!
   Fa la la la la la la la la.
   'Tis the season to be Jolly,
   Fa la la la la la la la la.
   Don we now our gay apparel,
   Fa la la la la la la la la.
   Troll the ancient Yule-tide carol,
   Fa la la la la la la la.

2. See the blazing Yule before us,
   Fa la la la la la la la la.
   Strike the harp and join the chorus,
   Fa la la la la la la la.
   Follow me in merry measure,
   Fa la la la la la la la.
   While I tell of Yule-tide treasure,
   Fa la la la la la la la.

3. Fast away the old year passes,
   Fa la la la la la la la la.
   Hail the new, ye lads and lasses,
   Fa la la la la la la la la.
   Sing we joyous all together,
   Fa la la la la la la la la.
   Heedless of the wind and weather,
   Fa la la la la la la la la.

Old Welsh Carol

GP337

The First Nowell

1. The first Nowell, the angels did say,
   Was to certain poor shepherds in fields as they lay,
   In fields where they lay keeping their sheep,
   On a cold winter's night that was so deep.

Refrain:
Nowell, Nowell, Nowell, Nowell,
Born is the King of Israel!

Old English Carol

Serenely

2. They looked up and saw a star
   Shining in the east beyond them far,
   And to the earth it gave great light,
   And so it continued both day and night.

3. And by the light of that same star,
   Three Wise Men came from a country afar,
   To seek for a king was their intent,
   And to follow the star wherever it went.

GP337

God Rest Ye Merry, Gentlemen

1. God rest ye merry, gentlemen,
Let nothing you dismay,
Remember Christ our Savior
Was born on Christmas Day;
To save us all from Satan's pow'r
When we were gone astray.

Refrain:
O tidings of comfort and joy,
Comfort and joy,
O tidings of comfort and joy.

Traditional English Carol

2. From God our heav'nly father
A blessed angel came;
And unto certain shepherds
Brought tidings of the same;
How that in Bethlehem was born
The Son of God by name.

3. Now to the Lord sing praises,
All you within this place,
And with true love and brotherhood
Each other now embrace;
This holy tide of Christmas
All others doth deface.

Good Christian Men, Rejoice

1. Good Christian men, rejoice
   With heart and soul and voice,
   Give ye heed to what we say:
   Jesus Christ is Born today!
   Christ is born today!
   Christ is born today!

2. Good Christian men, rejoice
   With heart and soul and voice,
   Now ye hear of endless bliss:
   Jesus Christ was born for this.
   Christ was born for this,
   Christ was born for this.

3. Good Christian men, rejoice
   With heart and soul and voice,
   Now ye need not fear the grave:
   Jesus Christ was born to save.
   Christ was born to save,
   Christ was born to save.

Old German Carol

Good King Wenceslas

1. Good King Wenceslas looked out,
   On the Feast of Stephen,
   When the snow lay round about,
   Deep, and crisp, and even:
   Brightly shone the moon that night,
   Though the frost was cruel,
   When a poor man came in sight,
   Gath'ring winter fuel.

2. "Bring me flesh, and bring me wine,
   Bring me pine logs hither:
   Thou and I will see him dine,
   When we bear them thither."
   Page and monarch, forth they went,
   Forth they went together;
   Through the rude wind's wild lament
   And the bitter weather.

With vigor

Hark! the Herald Angels Sing

1. Hark! the herald angels sing,
   "Glory to the newborn King;
   Peace on earth, and mercy mild,
   God and sinners reconciled!"
   Joyful, all ye nations, rise,
   Join the triumph of the skies;
   With th' angelic host proclaim,
   "Christ is born in Bethlehem!"

Refrain:
Hark! the herald angels sing,
"Glory to the newborn King!"

Words: Charles Wesley

Music: Felix Mendelssohn

2. Christ, by highest heaven adored;
   Christ, the Everlasting Lord!
   Late in time behold him come,
   Offspring of the Virgin's womb:
   Veiled in flesh the Godhead see;
   Hail th' Incarnate Diety,
   Pleased as man with men to dwell,
   Jesus, our Emmanuel.

3. Mild He lays his glory by,
   Born that man no more may die,
   Born to raise the sons of earth,
   Born to give them second birth.
   Risen with healing in His wings.
   Light and life to all He brings,
   Hail the Sun of Righteousness!
   Hail the heaven-born Prince of Peace!

He is Born, the Child Divine

1. He is born, the child divine;
   Play the oboe, sound the bagpipes.
   He is born, the child divine;
   Join in song, for the Lord has come.

   Refrain:
   Through long ages of the past,
   Prophets have foretold His coming;
   Through long ages of the past,
   Now the time has come at last!

2. O how lovely, O how pure,
   Is this perfect Child of Heaven;
   O how lovely, O how pure,
   Gracious gift of God to man!

3. Jesus, Lord of all the world,
   Coming as a Child among us,
   Jesus, Lord of all the world,
   Grant to us Thy heav'nly peace.

French Carol

A Holly Jolly Christmas

Have a Holly Jolly Christmas,
It's the best time of the year.
I don't know if there'll be snow
But have a cup of cheer.
Have a Holly Jolly Christmas,
And when you walk down the street
Say hello to friends you know
And everyone you meet.

Oh, ho, the mistletoe
Hung where you can see,
Somebody waits for you,
Kiss her once for me.
Have a Holly Jolly Christmas,
And in case you did not hear,
Oh, by golly, have a Holly Jolly
Christmas this year.

Johnny Marks

I Saw Three Ships

1. I saw three ships come sailing in,
   On Christmas Day, on Christmas Day;
   I saw three ships come sailing in,
   On Christmas Day in the morning.

2. And what was in those ships all three,
   On Christmas Day, on Christmas Day?
   And what was in those ships all three,
   On Christmas Day in the morning?

Traditional English Carol

3. Our Savior Christ and his ladie,
   On Christmas Day, on Christmas Day;
   Our Savior Christ and his ladie,
   On Christmas Day in the morning.

It Came Upon a Midnight Clear

1. It came upon a midnight clear,
That glorious song of old,
From angels bending near the earth,
To touch their harps of gold:
"Peace on the earth, goodwill to men,
From heaven's all-gracious King":
The world in solemn stillness lay,
To hear the angels sing.

2. Still through the cloven skies they come,
With peaceful wings unfurled,
And still their heavenly music floats
O'er all the weary world:
Above its sad and lowly plains
They bend on hovering wing,
And ever o'er its Babel sounds
The blessed angels sing.

Words: Edmund H. Sears

Music: Richard S. Willis

3. For lo, the days are hastening on,
   By prophet bards foretold,
   When with the ever-circling years
   Comes round the age of gold;
   When peace shall over all the earth
   Its ancient splendors fling,
   And the whole world give back the song
   Which now the angels sing.

Jingle Bells

1. Dashing through the snow
   In a one-horse open sleigh,
   O'er the fields we go,
   Laughing all the way.
   Bells on bobtail ring,
   Making spirits bright.
   What fun it is to ride and sing
   A sleighing song tonight. Oh,

Refrain:
Jingle bells, jingle bells,
Jingle all the way.
Oh, what fun it is to ride
In a one-horse open sleigh!
Jingle bells, jingle bells,
Jingle all the way.
Oh, what fun it is to ride
In a one-horse open sleigh!

John Pierpont

Jolly Old St. Nicolas

1. Jolly old St. Nicolas,
   Lean your ear this way!
   Don't you tell a single soul,
   What I'm going to say;
   Christmas eve is coming soon;
   Now, you dear old man,
   Whisper what you'll bring to me;
   Tell me if you can.

2. When the clock is striking twelve,
   When I'm fast asleep,
   Down the chimney broad and black,
   With your pack you'll creep;
   All the stockings you will find
   Hanging in a row;
   Mine will be the shortest one,
   You'll be sure to know.

3. Johnny wants a pair of skates;
   Susie wants a sled;
   Nellie wants a picture book;
   yellow, blue and red;
   Now I think I'll leave to you
   What to give the rest;
   Choose for me, dear Santa Claus,
   You will know the best.

American Carol

Joy to the World

1. Joy to the world! the Lord is come:
   Let earth receive her King;
   Let ev'ry heart prepare Him room,
   And heav'n and nature sing,
   And heav'n and nature sing,
   And heaven and heaven and nature sing.

2. Joy to the earth! the Savior reigns:
   Let men their songs employ;
   While fields and floods, rocks, hills, and plains
   Repeat the sounding joy,
   Repeat the sounding joy,
   Repeat, repeat the sounding joy.

3. He rules the world with truth and grace,
   And makes the nations prove
   The glories of His righteousness,
   And wonders of His love,
   And wonders of His love,
   And wonders, wonders of His love.

Words: Isaac Watts

Music: George F. Handel

Lo, How a Rose E'er Blooming

1. Lo, how a Rose e'er blooming
   From tender stem hath sprung!
   Of Jesse's lineage coming
   As men of old have sung.
   It came, a flow'ret bright,
   Amid the cold of winter,
   When halfspent was the night.

2. Isaiah 'twas foretold it,
   The Rose I have in mind;
   With Mary we behold it,
   The virgin mother kind.
   To show God's love aright
   She bore to men a Savior,
   When halfspent was the night.

3. This flow'r, whose fragrance tender
   With sweetness fills the air,
   Dispels with glorious splendor
   The darkness ev'rywhere.
   True man, yet very God,
   From sin and death he saves us
   And lightens ev'ry load.

16th Century Melody

Lullaby
(Joseph Dear, Oh, Joseph Mine)

1. Joseph Dear, Oh, Joseph Mine
   Help me lull the Babe Divine
   God in Heaven from above
   Has sent His love
   The new-born son of Mary

2. Let the harp with psalter ring,
   Praises to the gentle King
   Raise your voices all in one
   To glorify
   The birth of Christ, the infant Son.

Sweetly

poco rit.   L.H.

GP337

March of the Kings

This great day, I met upon the way,
The Kings of East as they came riding proudly,
This great day, I met upon the way,
The Kings of East with all their fine array.

The gifts of gold, frankincense, and myrrh
Were guarded close by a band of sturdy warriors,
Their swords, their shields, and their bucklers bright,
A-gleam and sparkling in the morning light.

13th Century Provencal Carol

O Christmas Tree

1. O Christmas tree! O Christmas tree!
   You stand in woodland beauty;
   O Christmas tree! O Christmas tree!
   You stand in woodland beauty;
   You are as green in winter's glow,
   As in the summer's richest glow;
   O Christmas tree! O Christmas tree!
   You stand in woodland beauty.

2. O Christmas tree! O Christmas tree!
   With faithful leaves unchanging.
   O Christmas tree! O Christmas tree!
   With faithful leaves unchanging.
   You are as green in winter's glow,
   As in the summer's richest glow;
   O Christmas tree! O Christmas tree!
   You stand in woodland beauty.

Old German Carol

O Come, All Ye Faithful

1. O come, all ye faithful,
   Joyful and triumphant,
   O come ye, O come ye to Bethlehem!
   Come and behold Him,
   Born the King of angels!

   Refrain:
   O come, let us adore Him,
   O come, let us adore Him,
   O come, let us adore Him,
   Christ the Lord!

2. O sing, choirs of angels,
   Sing in exultation!
   O sing, all ye citizens of heav'n above!
   Glory to God, all
   Glory in the highest!

3. Amen, Lord, we greet Thee,
   Born this happy morning,
   O Jesus, forever be Thy Name adored;
   Word of the Father,
   Now in flesh appearing!

O Come, O Come, Emmanuel

1. O come, O come, Emmanuel,
   And ransom captive Israel,
   That mourns in lonely exile here
   Until the Son of God appear.

   Refrain:
   Rejoice! Rejoice!
   Emmanuel shall come to thee,
   O Israel!

2. O come, thou Day spring, come and cheer,
   Our spirits by thine advent here;
   Disperse the gloomy clouds of night,
   And death's dark shadows put to flight.

3. O come, thou Key of David,
   And open wide our heavenly home;
   Make safe the way that leads on high,
   And close the path to misery.

Words: 9th Century Latin Hymn

Music: 13th Century Plainsong

GP337

O Holy Night

1. O holy night! the stars are brightly shining,
It is the night of our dear Savior's birth.
Long lay the world in sin and error pining,
Til He appear'd and the soul felt its worth.
A thrill of hope the weary world rejoices

For yonder breaks a new and glorious morn.
Fall on your knees! O hear the angel voices,
O night divine, O night when Christ was born,
O night divine, O night, O night divine.

Adolphe Adam

* High notes of the L.H. may often be played with the R.H.

2. Led by the light of faith serenely beaming,
With glowing hearts by His cradle we stand.
So, led by light of a star sweetly gleaming,
Here come the wise men from the Orient land.
The King of kings lay thus in lowly manger,

In all our trials born to be our friend.
He knows our need, to our weakness no stranger;
Behold your King, before the lowly bend.
Behold your King, your King, before Him bend.

O Little Town of Bethlehem

1. O little town of Bethlehem,
   How still we see thee lie;
   Above thy deep and dreamless sleep
   The silent stars go by:
   Yet in thy dark streets shineth
   The Everlasting Light;
   The hopes and fears of all the years
   Are met in thee tonight.

2. For Christ is born of Mary,
   And gathered all above,
   While mortals sleep, the angels keep
   Their watch of wondering love.
   O morning stars, together
   Proclaim the holy birth!
   And praises sing to God the King,
   And peace to men on earth!

3. O holy Child of Bethlehem!
   Descend to us, we pray;
   Cast out our sin, and enter in,
   Be born in us today.
   We hear the Christmas angels
   The great glad tidings tell;
   O come to us, abide with us,
   Our Lord Emmanuel!

Words: Phillips Brooks

Music: Lewis H. Redner

Pat-a-Pan

1. Willie, take your little drum,
With your whistle, Robin, come!
When we hear the fife and drum,
Ture-lure-lu, pata-pata-pan,
When we hear the fife and drum,
Christmas should be frolicsome.

2. Thus the men of olden days
Gave the King of kings their praise:
When they hear the fife and drum,
Ture-lure-lu, pata-pata-pan,
When they hear the fife and drum,
Sure our children won't be dumb!

3. God and man are now become
More at one than fife and drum.
When you hear the fife and drum,
Ture-lure-lu, pata-pata-pan,
When you hear the fife and drum,
Dance, and make the village hum!

Words: Bernard de la Mannoye

Music: 17th Century Burgundian

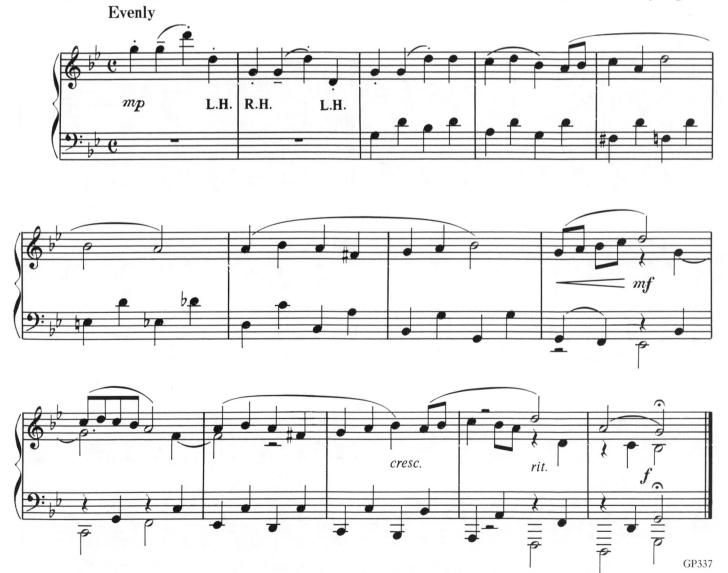

GP337

Rudolph the Red-Nosed Reindeer

Rudolph the red-nosed reindeer had a very shiny nose,
And if you ever saw it, you would even say it glowed,
All of the other reindeer used to laugh and call him names;
They never let poor Rudolph join in any reindeer games.

Johnny Marks

GP337

Then one foggy Christmas eve Santa came to say,
"Rudolph, with your nose so bright, won't you guide my sleigh tonight?"
Then, how the reindeer loved him, as they shouted out with glee,
"Rudolph, the red-nosed reindeer, you'll go down in history!"

Silent Night

1. Silent night, holy night,
   All is calm, all is bright,
   Round yon virgin mother and child.
   Holy infant so tender and mild,
   Sleep in heavenly peace,
   Sleep in heavenly peace.

2. Silent night, holy night,
   Shepherds quake at the sight,
   Glories stream from heaven afar,
   Heavn'ly hosts sing alleluia;
   Christ, the Savior is born!
   Christ, the Savior is born!

3. Silent night, holy night,
   Son of God, love's pure light
   Radiant beams from thy holy face,
   With the dawn of redeeming grace,
   Jesus, Lord, at thy birth,
   Jesus, Lord, at thy birth.

Words: Joseph Mohr

Music: Franz Gruber

The Sleep of the Infant Jesus

1. Here 'twixt the ass and oxen mild,
   Sleep, sleep,
   Sleep Thou little child:
   Thousand cherubim, thousand seraphim,
   Hover high above the mighty Lord of Love.

2. Here, with the rose and lily bright,
   Sleep, sleep,
   Sleep Thou little child:
   Thousand cherubim, thousand seraphim,
   Hover high above the mighty Lord of Love.

French Carol

Wistfully

We Three Kings

1. We three kings of Orient are,
   Bearing gifts we traverse afar,
   Field and fountain, moor and mountain,
   Following yonder star.

Refrain:
O, star of wonder, star of night,
Star with royal beauty bright,
Westward leading, still proceeding,
Guide us to thy perfect light.

John Henry Hopkins

2. Born a King on Bethlehem's plain,
   Gold I bring to crown him again
   King forever, ceasing never,
   Over us all to reign.

3. Frankincense to offer have I,
   Incense owns a Deity nigh;
   Prayer and praising, all men raising,
   Worship him, God on high.

What Child Is This!

to Justin

1. What child is this who, laid to rest,
On Mary's lap is sleeping,
Whom angels greet with anthems sweet,
While shepherds watch are keeping?

This, this is Christ the King;
Whom shepherds guard and angels sing:
Haste, haste to bring Him laud,
The Babe, the Son of Mary.

Words: William C. Dix

Music: Traditional English Folksong

GP337

2. Why lies He in such mean estate,
   Where ox and ass are feeding?
   Good Christian, fear: for sinners here
   The silent Word is pleading:

Nails, spear, shall pierce Him through,
The Cross be borne, for me, for you:
Hail, hail the Word made flesh,
The Babe, the Son of Mary!

Up on the Housetop

1. Up on the housetop reindeer pause,
   Out jumps good old Santa Claus;
   Down through the chimney with lots of toys,
   All for the little ones, Christmas joys.

   Refrain:
   Ho, ho, ho! Who wouldn't go!
   Ho, ho, ho! Who wouldn't go!
   Up on the housetop, click, click, click,
   Down through the chimney with good Saint Nick.

2. First comes the stocking of little Nell;
   Oh dear Santa fill it well;
   Give her a dollie that laughs and crys,
   One that will open and shut her eyes.

3. Next comes the stocking of little Will;
   Oh, just see what a glorious fill!
   Here is a hammer and lots of tacks,
   Also a ball and a whip that cracks.

B. R. Hanby